Tales from Pontypandy

EGMONT

We bring stories to life

First published in Great Britain in 2013 by Dean,
an imprint of Egmont UK Limited
The Yellow Building, 1 Nicholas Road, London W11 4AN

HIT entertainment

ISBN 978 0 6035 6800 8
54124/1
Printed in China

Tales from Pontypandy

This book belongs to

....

....

Contents

Meet the Characters

Elvis

Penny

Bronwyn

Charlie

Fireman Sam

Sarah

James

Tom
Thomas

Station
Officer
Steele

Dilys

Trevor

Mike

Helen

Norman

Mandy

The Great Fire of Pontypandy

It was a special day in Pontypandy.

Chief Fire Officer Boyce had come all the way from Newtown to give Fireman Sam a medal for bravery. "Well done, Sam!" he said.

"Thank you, sir!" replied Sam.

Station Officer Steele and the rest of the fire crew were very proud of Sam. He was a hero!

After the ceremony, Chief Fire Officer Boyce asked Sam to be the Station Officer in Newtown.

Sam knew that being a Station Officer was a very important job. But he wasn't sure that he wanted to move away from Pontypandy.

"I need time to think about the job," Sam told Officer Boyce.

Later, Sam, Elvis and Radar went to the forest. They put up signs to remind people not to light campfires.

With the weather so hot and dry, a forest fire could spread quickly. Pontypandy would be in great danger!

Before Sam returned to the Fire Station, Elvis asked him, "I'd like to be a hero too. How do you do it?"

"I'm not sure, Elvis," Sam replied with surprise. "I just try to be the best firefighter I can be."

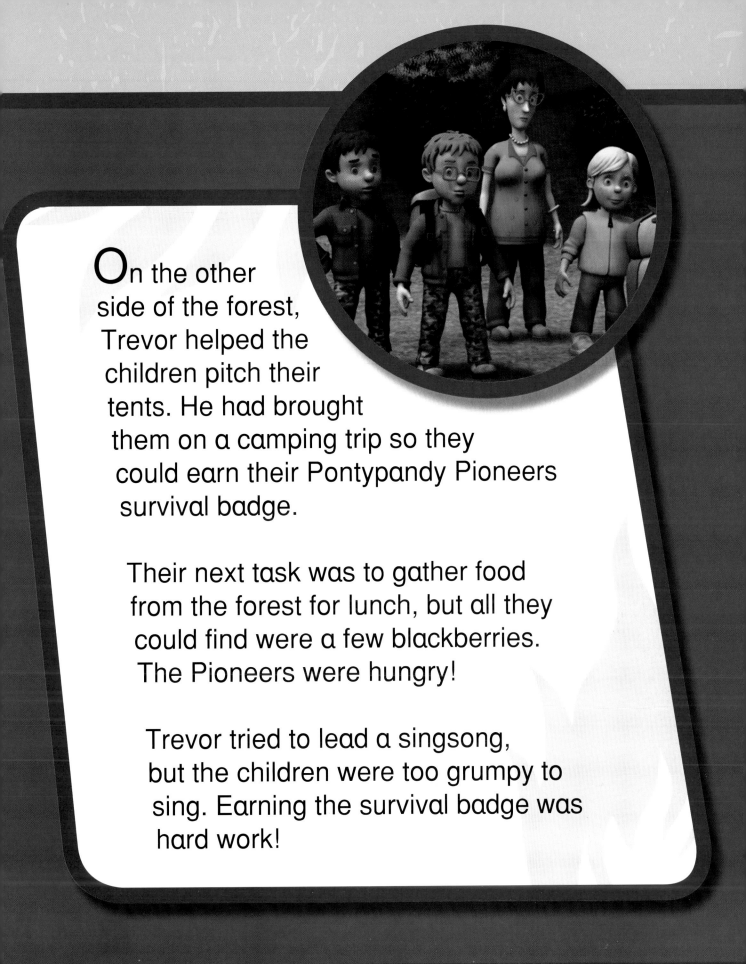

On the other side of the forest, Trevor helped the children pitch their tents. He had brought them on a camping trip so they could earn their Pontypandy Pioneers survival badge.

Their next task was to gather food from the forest for lunch, but all they could find were a few blackberries. The Pioneers were hungry!

Trevor tried to lead a singsong, but the children were too grumpy to sing. Earning the survival badge was hard work!

Norman and his cousin had secretly brought some sausages on the trip. They sneaked away to find a place to cook them.

"But there are no fires allowed," Derek said.

"We can't eat raw sausages, can we!" Norman replied as he rubbed two sticks together.

"Norman!" It was his mum, Dilys!
The boys left the sticks and
ran back to the camp.
Suddenly, the sticks
burst into flames!

At the Mountain Rescue Station, Tom Thomas looked out of the window. He spotted a strange cloud over the forest and looked closer.

It wasn't a cloud, it was smoke from a fire! Tom called the Fire Station straight away.

"Tom here. I see smoke in the forest," he reported to Station Officer Steele. "I'll try and put out the fire before it spreads."

With Sam gone, Elvis put up the last of the signs. Suddenly, Elvis' walkie-talkie crackled.

"Cridlington!" shouted Station Officer Steele. "A forest fire has started and there are people on the campsite. You must get them out of danger!"

"You can count on me, sir!" Elvis said.
"Let's go, Radar!"

Tom flew Wallaby One over the forest and dropped an enormous bucket of water on to the flames.

"Tom," Sam said over the walkie-talkie, "how does it look?"

"Not good, Sam," answered Tom. "The wind is blowing the fire towards Pontypandy!"

"We'll be right there to tackle it from the ground," promised Sam.

With the lights flashing and sirens wailing, Jupiter and Venus sped into the forest.

Sam, Penny and Station Officer Steele sprayed water on the trees and grass. They hoped that it would stop the flames.

If the fire spread, Pontypandy could be destroyed. It was up to Sam and the crew to save the town!

"Steady now!" called Sam. Fighting this fire would take a lot of teamwork!

Meanwhile, Elvis asked Radar to sniff around the forest. With his clever nose, Radar soon led Elvis to the campers!

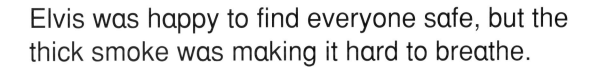

Elvis was happy to find everyone safe, but the thick smoke was making it hard to breathe.

"Follow me!" said Elvis. He heard Jupiter's siren and led the group towards the sound. Finally, they found their way out of the smoky woods.

"Well done, Elvis!" said Sam.

Elvis joined the fire crew battling the blaze, but it was too strong for the water hoses.

Crack! Suddenly, a burning branch broke off a tree and fell straight towards Sam!

Without thinking, Elvis knocked right into Sam and rolled him to safety. The branch landed on the spot where Sam had been standing.

"Thanks, Elvis!" cried Sam. "You saved my life!"

Despite the crew's hard work, the fire was still heading for Pontypandy.

"We must get everyone to safety!" called Station Officer Steele.

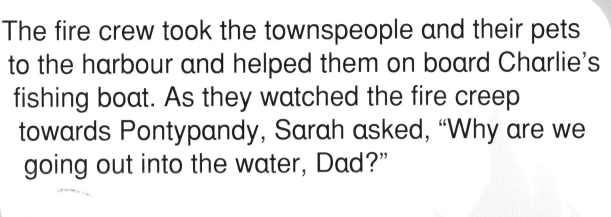

The fire crew took the townspeople and their pets to the harbour and helped them on board Charlie's fishing boat. As they watched the fire creep towards Pontypandy, Sarah asked, "Why are we going out into the water, Dad?"

"It's the only place where the fire can't reach us," said Charlie.

As the fire got closer, Sam felt very sad.
He didn't want to see Pontypandy destroyed.

Just then a drop of water fell on his nose.
Sam looked up at the clouds. "It's raining!"
he shouted.

"Let's hope it's enough to put out the fire!" said Penny, as the rain began to pour down.

Tom soon radioed from his helicopter. "The rain has put out the fire. We're out of danger!"

The townspeople cheered as the boat returned to the dock. Pontypandy was safe!

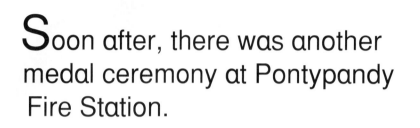

Soon after, there was another medal ceremony at Pontypandy Fire Station.

"Elvis, you showed real bravery during the Great Fire," Boyce said. "Well done!"

Elvis saluted. Now he was a hero, too!

"And it's my pleasure to give survival badges to the Pontypandy Pioneers," Trevor Evans said next. "Well, to most of them . . ."

"This is all your fault!"
Norman and Derek
moaned to each other.
There were no badges
for them.

Afterwards, Sam told Chief Fire Officer Boyce that he had decided not to take the job in Newtown.

"Why didn't you take it, Sam?" Elvis asked him later. "You could have been a Station Officer in Newtown with your very own crew."

Fireman Sam smiled. "I learned a lot during the Great Fire, Elvis," he said. "I almost lost Pontypandy and now I know I never want to leave. Pontypandy will always be my home!"

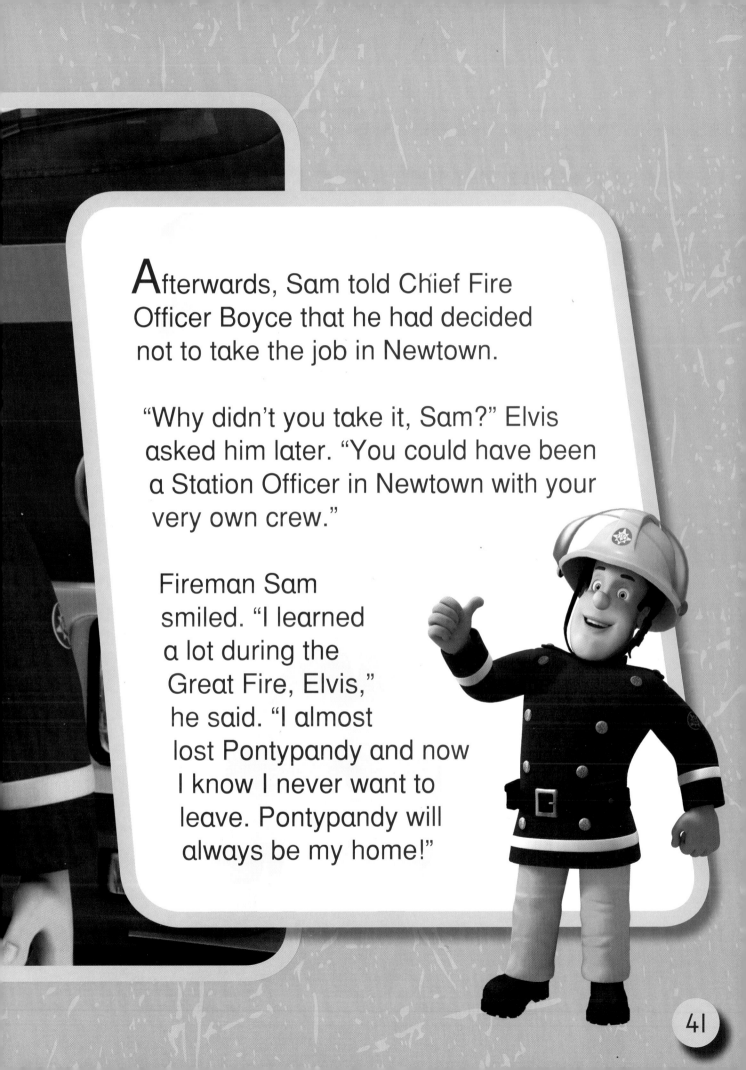

The Great Fire of Pontypandy Story Quiz

Can you answer the questions about the story?

1) What did Chief Fire Officer Boyce give Sam for bravery?

a)   a medal
b)   a trophy
c)   a badge

2) What were Norman and Derek trying to cook in the forest?

a)   toast
b)   sausages
c)   burgers

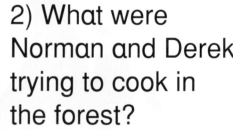

3) Where did the Great Fire start?

a) on the beach
b) in Dilys' shop
c) in the forest

4) What did Fireman Sam and the crew use to try to put the Great Fire out?

a) fire extinguishers
b) hoses
c) sand

Answers on page 79

The Pontypandy Flood

It was a beautiful morning in Pontypandy. The sun was shining, the birds were singing and in his bedroom over his mum's shop, Norman Price had just woken up.

Norman hated getting up early. He yawned and stretched as he pulled on his clothes, before shuffling over to his bedroom window.

When he pulled the curtains apart, Norman couldn't believe what he saw. Charlie's fishing boat was outside his bedroom window!

Norman ran downstairs to find his mum standing on the shop counter with water all around. "Mam!" he told her, "I think the whole town is flooded!"

Dilys thought for a moment. "You'd better get back upstairs," she said. "I'll ring the Fire Station to find out what to do."

But Norman had other things on his mind. "Do you think Woolly and Lambikins will be all right in their field?" Norman asked.

"I'm sure they'll be fine," Dilys said as she searched a shelf for her mobile phone.

Meanwhile, up in Wallaby One, Fireman Sam and Tom Thomas were flying across Pontypandy, looking down at the damage.

"This is the worst high tide I have ever seen," Sam told Tom.

"And it won't go out again for four hours,"
Tom replied as he looked at the water below.
It stretched from the Quayside to the centre
of the town and beyond.

"I think we are going to have a busy day!" Sam said.

Just then, Wallaby One's radio crackled and Station Officer Steele's voice boomed out.

"The Jones family went on to the roof to escape the flood," he told Sam and Tom. "Now they are stuck and need help getting to safety."

"We're on our way, Sir!" Sam replied as Tom steered Wallaby One towards the Quayside.

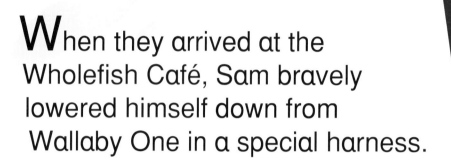

When they arrived at the Wholefish Café, Sam bravely lowered himself down from Wallaby One in a special harness.

"Is everyone all right?" Sam asked.

"We're OK," Bronwyn replied. "But we can't find Lion!"

"I'm sure he'll be fine – he's a clever cat," said Sam. "Let's get you all back to the station."

And so, one by one, Sam winched the Jones family to safety.

At the same time, Penny and Elvis were steering Neptune through the flooded streets to help anyone in need. They found Trevor stranded on top of his bus.

"I'm glad to see you!" Trevor said as he wriggled down and landed softly on board Neptune.

The three of them set off towards the Fire Station.

Back in his bedroom, Norman was still worried about Woolly and Lambikins. As he gazed out of his window towards their field, something caught his eye. A small rowing boat had drifted under his window. Norman looked at it for a moment and an idea popped into his head.

"I'll go to the field and save them myself!" he said aloud. Soon he was shimmying down a rope made of knotted bedsheets, into the boat.

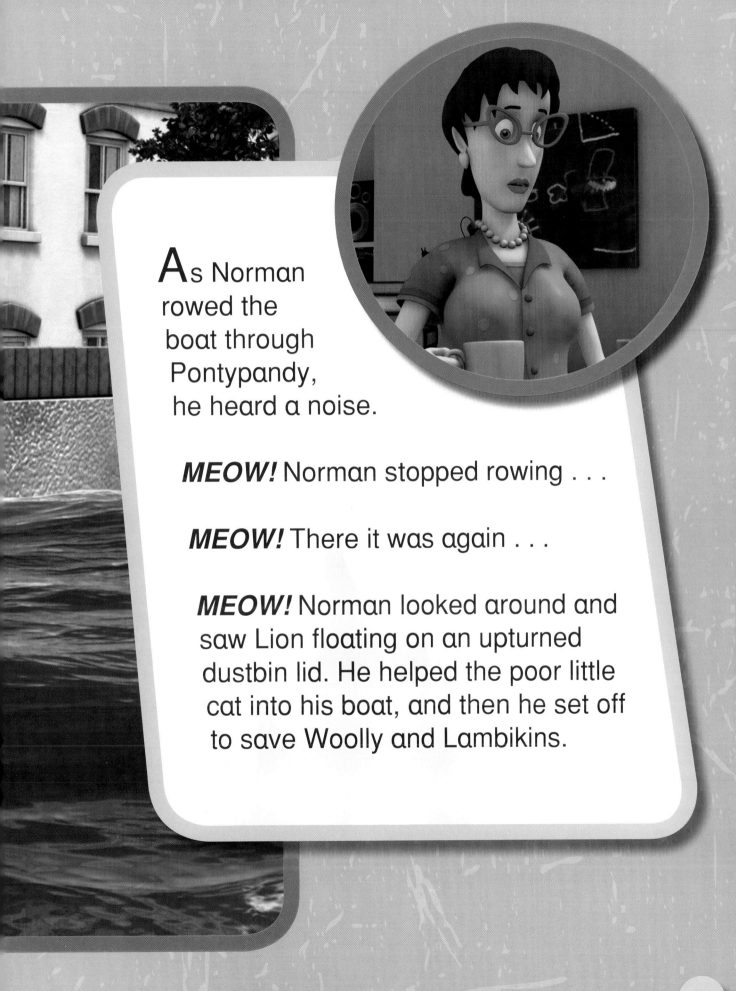

As Norman rowed the boat through Pontypandy, he heard a noise.

MEOW! Norman stopped rowing . . .

MEOW! There it was again . . .

MEOW! Norman looked around and saw Lion floating on an upturned dustbin lid. He helped the poor little cat into his boat, and then he set off to save Woolly and Lambikins.

Penny, Elvis and Trevor were sailing past the shop in Neptune when Dilys rushed out. "Help!" she called. "Norman's disappeared!"

In a panic, Trevor jumped down from Neptune. "Don't worry, Dilys!" he said. "I'm here to help!"

But Dilys wasn't listening. "He was worried about Woolly and Lambikins," she told Penny and Elvis. "I think he may have gone to save them!"

"We need to talk to Wallaby One!" gasped Penny as she grabbed the lifeboat's radio.
"Penny to Sam . . . do you hear me?"

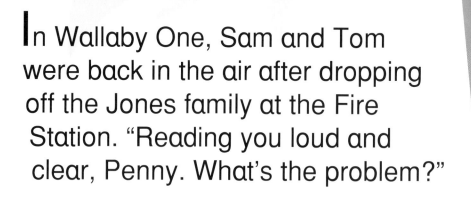

In Wallaby One, Sam and Tom were back in the air after dropping off the Jones family at the Fire Station. "Reading you loud and clear, Penny. What's the problem?"

"Norman has gone out alone in the flood water to look for his sheep," Penny said over the radio.

"OK, Penny, we'll start a search operation from up here while you and Elvis search in Neptune," Sam said calmly. And with that, Tom swooped Wallaby One back over the town and towards the fields.

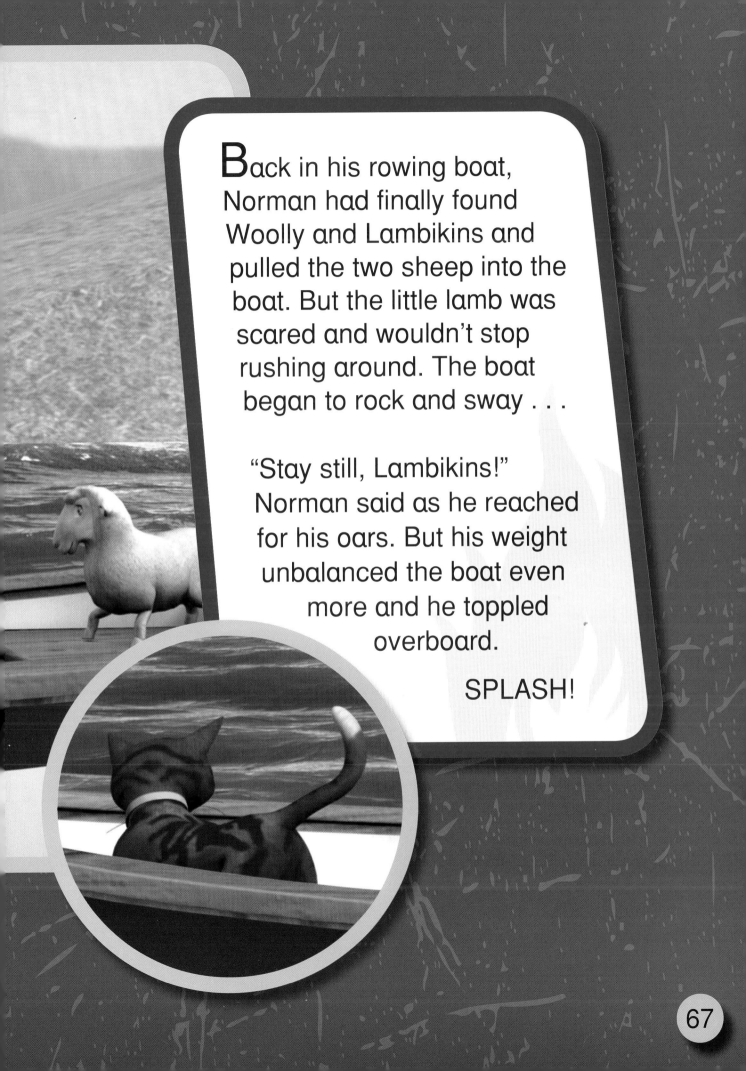

Back in his rowing boat, Norman had finally found Woolly and Lambikins and pulled the two sheep into the boat. But the little lamb was scared and wouldn't stop rushing around. The boat began to rock and sway . . .

"Stay still, Lambikins!" Norman said as he reached for his oars. But his weight unbalanced the boat even more and he toppled overboard.

SPLASH!

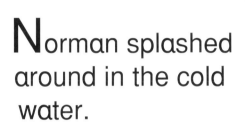

Norman splashed around in the cold water.

"Help!" he shouted as loudly as he could, but there was no one around to hear him. As he thrashed around in the water, the boat began to drift away from him, taking Woolly, Lambikins and Lion with it.

Up in Wallaby One, Sam and Tom were zooming across the bay when they saw something below. It was Norman!

Sam grabbed the radio. "Sam to Penny," he said. "Norman is in the water at Breaker's Field. This is an emergency!"

"Penny to Sam," came her reply. "We'll get there straight away!"

Back in Neptune, Elvis and Dilys held on tightly as Penny cranked the lifeboat's engine up to full speed. Soon they were skimming across the water towards Breaker's Field.

When they saw Norman, Penny slowed down before Elvis pulled him out of the water.

"It's a good job you're wearing your lifejacket, Norman," said Penny.

"Thanks for saving me," he replied. "But we need to get Woolly, Lambikins and Lion too!" The animals were still floating out to sea!

Penny whizzed to the rescue! The animals were very scared, but Norman spoke to them softly as Penny gently lifted them into the lifeboat. They were safe at last!

Back at the Fire Station, everyone was pleased to see Norman and the animals safe and well. The tide was going out, and the flood waters were going down.

"You shouldn't have gone out in the flood," Station Officer Steele told Norman sternly. "You were in real danger out there."

"But you were very brave for saving the animals," Fireman Sam said kindly, "even if we had to save you in the end!"

The Pontypandy Flood Story Quiz

Can you answer the questions about the story?

1) What did Norman see when he looked out of his bedroom window?

a) Charlie's fishing boat
b) Trevor's bus
c) Fireman Sam in Jupiter

2) Where was Trevor rescued from?
a) the shop
b) the café
c) the roof of his bus

3) Who did Norman rescue from the flood?

a) Sarah and James
b) Radar
c) Woolly, Lambikins and Lion

4) Where was Noman found by Penny and Elvis?

a) Breaker's Field
b) the Quayside
c) his mum's shop

Answers on page 79

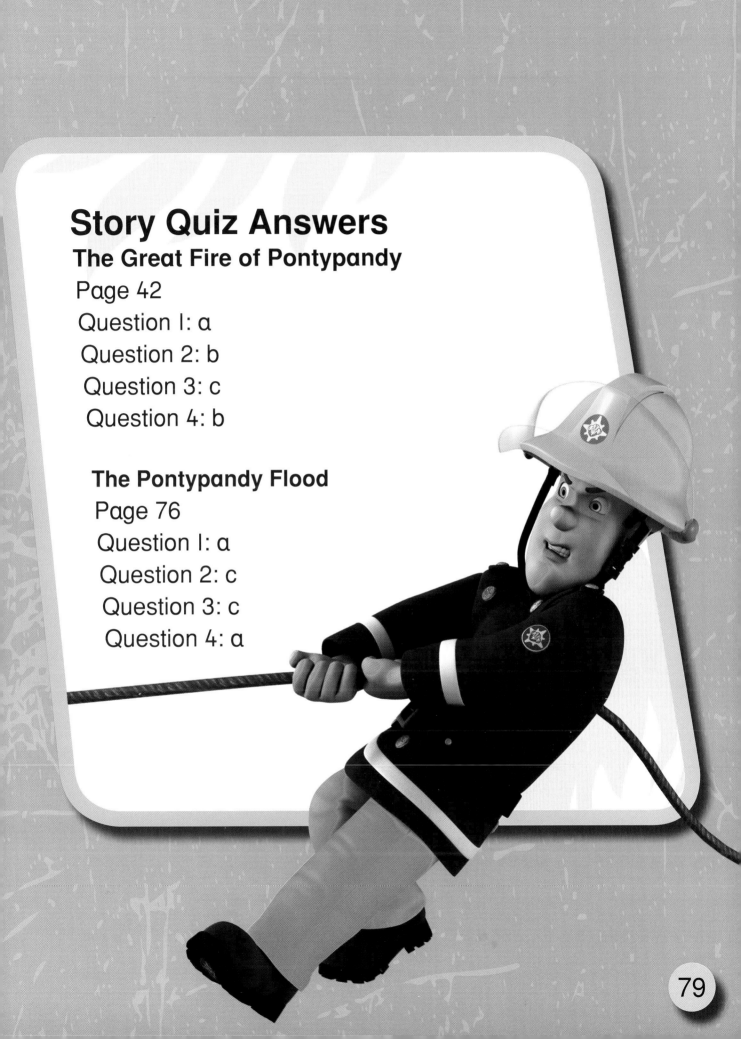

Story Quiz Answers

The Great Fire of Pontypandy

Page 42

Question 1: a

Question 2: b

Question 3: c

Question 4: b

The Pontypandy Flood

Page 76

Question 1: a

Question 2: c

Question 3: c

Question 4: a

Goodbye!